# SCOTTISH TEAS

## RECIPES FROM SCOTLAND

**Sue McDougall**

## DOMINO BOOKS (WALES) LTD

# METRIC/IMPERIAL/AMERICAN UNITS

We are all used to doubling or halving a recipe. Thus, a Victoria sandwich may be made using 4 oz each of flour, sugar and butter with 2 eggs or 6 oz each of flour, sugar and butter with 3 eggs. The proportions of the ingredients are unchanged. This must be so for all units. Use either the metric units or the imperial units given in the recipes, do not mix the two.

It is not practical to give the exact equivalents of metric and imperial units because 1 oz equals 28.35 g and 1 pint equals 568 ml. The tables on page vi indicate suitable quantities but liquids should be carefully added to obtain the correct consistency. See also the charts on page iv.

## PINTS TO MILLILITRES AND LITRES
### The following are approximations only

¼ pint = 150 ml

½ pint = 275 ml

¾ pint = 425 ml

1 pint = 575 ml

1¾ pints = 1000 ml (1 litre)

3 pints = 1½ litres

© D C P and E J P, 1997, 1998, 1999, 2000
Domino Books (Wales) Ltd
P O Box 32
Swansea SA1 1FN
UK
Tel. 01792 459378
Fax 01792 466337

# CONTENTS

The following charts give the approximate equivalents for metric and imperial weights, and oven temperatures.

| Ounces | Approx g to nearest whole number | Approx g to nearest whole 25 g |
|--------|----------------------------------|--------------------------------|
| 1      | 28                               | 25                             |
| 2      | 57                               | 50                             |
| 3      | 85                               | 75                             |
| 4      | 113                              | 125                            |
| 5      | 142                              | 150                            |
| 6      | 170                              | 175                            |
| 7      | 198                              | 200                            |
| 8      | 226                              | 225                            |
| 9      | 255                              | 250                            |
| 10     | 283                              | 275                            |
| 11     | 311                              | 300                            |
| 12     | 340                              | 350                            |
| 13     | 368                              | 375                            |
| 14     | 396                              | 400                            |
| 15     | 428                              | 425                            |
| 16     | 456                              | 450                            |

**OVEN TEMPERATURE GUIDE**

|                  | Electricity °C | Electricity °F | Gas Mark |
|------------------|------|------|----------|
| Very cool        | 110  | 225  | $\frac{1}{4}$ |
|                  | 130  | 250  | $\frac{1}{2}$ |
| Cool             | 140  | 275  | 1        |
|                  | 150  | 300  | 2        |
| Moderate         | 170  | 325  | 3        |
|                  | 180  | 350  | 4        |
| Moderately hot   | 190  | 375  | 5        |
|                  | 200  | 400  | 6        |
| Hot              | 220  | 425  | 7        |
|                  | 230  | 450  | 8        |
| Very hot         | 240  | 475  | 9        |

When using this chart for weights over 16 ounces, add the appropriate figures in the column giving the nearest whole number of grammes and then adjust to the nearest unit of 25. For example, 18 oz (16 oz + 2 oz) becomes 456 + 57 = 513 to the nearest whole number and 500 g to the nearest unit of 25.

Throughout the book, 1 teaspoon = 5 ml and 1 tablespoon = 15 ml.

# FOREWORD

*The Scots are among the best cold-weather and high-tea-table cooks in the world.* The way of life and the culture of the people is reflected in a country's cooking. Traditional Scottish cooking is based on home-grown produce. The Scots know the importance and value of good, home cooking. Many recipes have been handed down. New technology and ideas influence the way in which food is prepared today and the traditional recipes in this book have been adapted to use these new methods.

Afternoon tea is a very enjoyable meal. It is a pause between the work of the day and the activities of the evening. It may start with sandwiches followed by cakes, scones or a bannock. Conserves, especially raspberry jam and heather honey with thick cream add to the enjoyment of the meal. Sometimes it is taken later, about six o'clock, as high tea. This usually includes savouries such as pies, cold meats accompanied by delicious relishes or tasty fish dishes as well as the delicate offerings of afternoon tea. This is a welcoming meal on chilly evenings as daylight fades.

Teatime is part of the Scottish way of life. I hope the recipes and ideas in this book will help you and your family and friends enjoy this most civilised, traditional occasion.

There are more Scottish recipes in the companion books, *Scottish Cooking, Customs and Cooking from Scotland* and *Celtic Recipes*.

S M

# AMERICAN MEASURES

American measures are given by volume and weight using standard cups and spoons.

**US Standard Measuring Spoons and Cups**

1 tablespoon = 3 teaspoons = ½ fluid ounce = 14.2 ml
2 tablespoons = 1 fluid ounce = 28 ml
4 tablespoons = ¼ cup
5 tablespoons = ⅓ cup
8 tablespoons = ½ cup
10 tablespoons = ⅔ cup
12 tablespoons = ¾ cup
16 tablespoons = 2 cups = 8 fluid ounces = ½ US pint
32 tablespoons = 2 cups = 16 fluid ounces = 1 US pint.

| Metric (Imperial) | American |
|---|---|
| 1 teaspoon | 1 teaspoon |
| 1 tablespoon | 1 tablespoon |
| 1½ teaspoons | 2 tablespoons |
| 2 tablespoons | 3 tablespoons |
| 3 tablespoons | ¼ (scant) cup |
| 4 tablespoons | 5 tablespoons |
| 5 tablespoons | 6 tablespoons |
| 5½ tablespoons | 7 tablespoons |
| 6 tablespoons (scant ¼ pint) | ½ cup |
| ¼ pint | ⅔ cup |
| scant ½ pint | 1 cup |
| ½ pint (10 fl oz) | 1¼ cups |
| ¾ pint (15 fl oz) | scant 2 cups |
| ¾ pint (16 fl oz) | 2 cups (1 pint) |
| 1 pint (20 fl oz) | 2½ cups |

| Metric (Imperial) | American |
|---|---|
| ***flour, plain or self-raising*** | |
| 15 g (½ oz) | 2 tablespoons |
| 25 g (1 oz) | 1¼ cup |
| 100/125 g (4 oz) | 1 cup |
| ***sugar, caster or granulated, brown (firmly packed)*** | |
| 25 g (1 oz) | 2 tablespoons |
| 100/125 g (4 oz) | ½ cup |
| 200/225 g (8 oz) | 1 cup |
| ***butter, margarine, fat*** | |
| 1 oz | 2 tablespoons |
| 225 g (8 oz) | 1 cup |
| 150 g (5 oz) shredded suet | 1 cup |

***1 cup (American) contains approximately***

100/125 g (4 oz) grated cheese, 50 g (2 oz) fresh breadcrumbs,
100 g (4 oz) dried breadcrumbs,
100/125 g (4 oz) pickled beetroot, button mushrooms, shelled peas, red/blackcurrants, 5 oz strawberries,
175 g (6 oz) raisins, currants, sultanas, chopped candied peel, stoned dates,
225 g (8 oz) glacé cherries, 150 g (5 oz) shelled whole walnuts,
100 g (4 oz) chopped nuts,
75 g (3 oz) desiccated coconut,
225 g (8 oz) cottage cheese,
100/125 g (4 oz) curry powder,
225 g (8 oz) minced raw meat,
⅜ pint (7½ fl oz) cream.

# CAKES

## RASPBERRY CREAM SPONGE CAKE

METRIC
*Sponge Cake*
*3 eggs*
*100 g caster sugar*
*75 g plain flour*
**Raspberry Cream Filling**
*450 ml whipping cream*
*2 tablespoons Drambuie (optional)*
*400 g Scottish raspberries*
*2 tablespoons raspberry jam*
*100 g flaked almonds, toasted*

IMPERIAL
*Sponge Cake*
*3 eggs*
*4 oz caster sugar*
*3 oz plain flour*
**Raspberry Cream Filling**
*$\frac{3}{4}$ pint whipping cream*
*2 tablespoons Drambuie (optional)*
*1 lb Scottish raspberries*
*2 tablespoons raspberry jam*
*4 oz flaked almonds, toasted*

**Sponge Cake** Grease two 18-cm (7 inch) sandwich tins and dust with a mixture of flour and caster sugar. Put the eggs and sugar in a large deep bowl and stand in a pan of hot water. Whisk until light and creamy. The mixture should retain the impression of the whisk for a few seconds. Remove from the heat and whisk until cold. Sift half the flour over the mixture and fold in very lightly using a metal spoon. Fold in the remaining flour. Pour the mixture in the tins and tilt the tins to spread it evenly. Bake in a moderately hot oven (180ºC, 375ºF, gas mark 5) for 20 - 25 minutes. Turn on to a wire rack to cool.

**Raspberry Cream Filling** Whip the cream until it just holds its shape. Sprinkle the Drambuie over the raspberries. Cut up half the raspberries and mix into the cream. Cover the top of one of the sponge cakes with jam. Place half of the raspberry/cream mixture on top of the jam and cover with the other sponge cake. Cover the top and sides of the cake with the remaining raspberry/cream mixture. Pile the remaining raspberries on top of the cake. Cover the side of the cake with the toasted almonds.

# CHOCOLATE STRAWBERRY CAKE

METRIC
*Cake*
75 g self raising flour
2 tablespoons ground rice
100 g plain chocolate (grated)
100 g butter
2 - 3 drops vanilla essence
2 eggs (beaten)
*Filling*
200 g strawberries
75 g plain chocolate
300 ml whipping cream
1 tablespoon icing sugar

IMPERIAL
*Cake*
3 oz self raising flour
2 tablespoons ground rice
4 g plain chocolate (grated)
4 oz butter
2 - 3 drops vanilla essence
2 eggs (beaten)
*Filling*
8 oz strawberries
3 oz plain chocolate
$\frac{1}{2}$ pint whipping cream
1 tablespoon icing sugar

**Cake** Grease and line a 15-cm (6-inch) cake tin. Mix the flour and ground rice. Place the grated chocolate into a basin standing over a saucepan of hot water and heat gently to melt the chocolate. Cream the butter, sugar and essence together until light and fluffy. Add the melted chocolate to the creamed mixture. [The chocolate should be just warm.] Mix together. Beat in the eggs one at a time. Fold in the flour/rice. Turn the mixture into the cake tin and bake in a moderate oven (180ºC, 350ºF, gas mark 4) for 1 - 1$\frac{1}{2}$ hours until firm to the touch. Turn on to a wire tray to cool. When cold split in half.

**Filling** Keep 4 strawberries to one side. Hull and wash the rest of the strawberries. Cut up half the fruit and grate 50 g (2 oz) of the chocolate. Lightly whip the cream. Mix half the cream with the chopped strawberries and grated chocolate. Use to sandwich the cake together. Cover the top of the cake with the rest of the cream. Melt the remaining chocolate. Wash the 4 reserved unhulled strawberries, dry then dip them in the chocolate. Pile the remaining strawberries on top of the cake and then add the chocolate coated fruit.

# DUNDEE CAKE

| METRIC | IMPERIAL |
|---|---|
| *150 g butter* | *6 oz butter* |
| *150 g brown sugar* | *6 oz brown sugar* |
| *grated rind of 1 lemon* | *grated rind of 1 lemon* |
| *4 eggs* | *4 eggs* |
| *200 g flour* | *8 oz flour* |
| *1 teaspoon baking powder* | *1 teaspoon baking powder* |
| *75 g currants* | *3 oz currants* |
| *75 g sultanas* | *3 oz sultanas* |
| *75 g raisins* | *3 oz raisins* |
| *50 g chopped mixed peel* | *2 oz chopped mixed peel* |
| *50 g blanched almonds* | *2 oz blanched almonds* |

Cream the butter and sugar until light and fluffy. Add the lemon rind. Beat the eggs and beat into the butter mixture. Sieve the flour and baking powder together. Fold the flour, fruit, peel and half the blanched almonds, chopped, into the mixture. Turn into a greased and lined 20 cm (8 inch) cake tin. Arrange the remaining almonds on top of the cake. Bake in a moderate oven (180ºC, 350ºF, gas mark 4) for 2 - 3 hours. If the top browns too quickly, cover with brown paper or greaseproof paper. Turn out and cool on a wire rack.

[There is an alternative recipe for Dundee Cake in *Scottish Cooking*.]

# GINGER PARKIN

| METRIC | IMPERIAL |
|---|---|
| 150 g flour | 6 oz flour |
| 1  teaspoon bicarbonate of soda | 1 teaspoon bicarbonate of soda |
| $\frac{1}{2}$ teaspoon mixed spice | $\frac{1}{2}$ teaspoon mixed spice |
| $\frac{1}{2}$ teaspoon cinnamon | $\frac{1}{2}$ teaspoon cinnamon |
| 1 teaspoon ground ginger | 1 teaspoon ground ginger |
| 200 g fine oatmeal | 8 oz fine oatmeal |
| 1 egg | 1 egg |
| 100 g butter | 4 oz butter |
| 150 g black treacle | 6 oz black treacle |
| 150 g brown sugar | 6 oz brown sugar |
| 5 tablespoons milk | 5 tablespoons milk |
| almonds | almonds |
| pinch of salt | pinch of salt |

Sift the flour, bicarbonate of soda, spices and salt together. Mix in the oatmeal. Lightly beat the egg. Warm the butter, treacle and sugar together in a saucepan and add with the egg to the oatmeal mixture. Mix well. Stir in enough milk to form a firm batter. Line a greased shallow rectangular tin with greased greaseproof paper. Turn the batter into the tin and smooth over. Bake in a moderate oven (180°C, 350°F, gas mark 4) for 25 minutes and then at 170°C, 325°F, gas mark 3 for a further 25 minutes. Mark into squares and place an almond on each. When cool cut into squares.

# GIRDLE PARKIN

METRIC
*150 g fine oatmeal*
*150 g flour*
*½ teaspoon cinnamon*
*½ teaspoon ground ginger*
*25 g butter*
*25 g sugar*
*2 tablespoons treacle*
*1 egg*
*milk*

IMPERIAL
*6 oz fine oatmeal*
*6 oz flour*
*½ teaspoon cinnamon*
*½ teaspoon ground ginger*
*1 oz butter*
*1 oz sugar*
*2 tablespoons treacle*
*1 egg*
*milk*

Mix all the dry ingredients together. Melt the butter, sugar and treacle and stir into the mixture. Lightly beat the egg. Add the egg and enough milk to give a thick dropping consistency. Drop a teaspoonful of the mixture at a time on to a hot girdle. Bake until lightly brown. Turn and cook on the other side. Cool on a wire tray.

# SWEET BANNOCKS

METRIC
*175 g fine oatmeal*
*100 g self-raising flour*
*100 g caster sugar*
*75 g butter*
*4 tablespoons water*

IMPERIAL
*7 oz fine oatmeal*
*4 oz self-raising flour*
*4 oz caster sugar*
*3 oz butter*
*4 tablespoons water*

Mix the dry ingredients together. Melt the butter with the water in a saucepan and pour into the centre of the oatmeal mixture. Mix well. Turn on to a floured board and roll out to a thickness of 0•75 cm (¼ inch). Cut into rounds and bake at 200°C, 400°F, gas mark 6 for 15 minutes. Turn off the oven and leave to cool in the oven. Serve with jam and cream.

# PITCAITHLY BANNOCK

| METRIC | IMPERIAL |
|---|---|
| *25 g blanched almonds* | *1 oz blanched almonds* |
| *25 g orange or citron peel* | *1 oz orange or citron peel* |
| *100 g butter* | *4 oz butter* |
| *75 g caster sugar* | *3 oz caster sugar* |
| *200 g flour* | *8 oz flour* |

Blanch and skin the almonds and finely chop the orange peel. Mix the nuts and peel together. Knead the butter and sugar together by hand. Work the flour, peel and nuts into the butter/sugar mixture by hand. Knead lightly until smooth. Press with the hand into a round about 1 cm ( $\frac{1}{2}$ inch thick). Place a lightly greased sheet of greaseproof paper on a baking sheet. Place the bannock on the baking sheet and cook in a warm oven (170°C, 325°F, gas mark 3) for 50 minutes. Sprinkle with caster sugar and cool on a wire tray.

# FIFE BANNOCKS

| METRIC | IMPERIAL |
|---|---|
| *150 g flour* | *6 oz flour* |
| *100 g oatmeal* | *4 oz oatmeal* |
| $\frac{1}{2}$ *teaspoon bicarbonate of soda* | $\frac{1}{2}$ *teaspoon bicarbonate of soda* |
| $\frac{1}{2}$ *teaspoon cream of tartar* | $\frac{1}{2}$ *teaspoon cream of tartar* |
| $\frac{1}{2}$ *teaspoon sugar* | $\frac{1}{2}$ *teaspoon sugar* |
| *10 g lard* | $\frac{1}{2}$ *oz lard* |
| *4 tablespoons buttermilk or thick sour milk* | *4 tablespoons buttermilk or thick sour milk* |
| *pinch salt* | *pinch salt* |

Mix all the dry ingredients together and rub in the lard. Add milk to make a soft dough. Turn on to a floured board and knead lightly. Roll into a round. Cut in four and bake on a hot girdle or a thick-bottomed frying pan.

# SCOTTISH BLACK BUN

| METRIC | IMPERIAL |
|---|---|
| **Shortcrust Pastry** | **Shortcrust Pastry** |
| **Filling** | **Filling** |
| 200 g plain flour | 8 oz plain flour |
| 1 teaspoon ground cinnamon | 1 teaspoon ground cinnamon |
| 1 teaspoon cream of tartar | 1 teaspoon cream of tartar |
| 1 teaspoon bicarbonate of soda | 1 teaspoon bicarbonate of soda |
| 100 g brown sugar | 4 oz brown sugar |
| 400 g seedless raisins | 1 lb seedless raisins |
| 400 g currants | 1 lb currants |
| 50 g chopped mixed peel | 2 oz chopped mixed peel |
| 100 g chopped blanched almonds | 4 oz chopped blanched almonds |
| 1 egg | 1 egg |
| 4 tablespoons milk | 4 tablespoons milk |
| 6 tablespoons whisky | 6 tablespoons whisky |

**Pastry:** Make the shortcrust pastry as on page 18. Grease a 20 cm (8 inch) cake tin. Roll out two-thirds of the pastry and line the tin so that the pastry comes above the edge of the tin. **Filling:** Sift the flour, spice, cream of tartar and bicarbonate of soda together. Stir in the sugar, fruit, chopped peel, almonds and mix well. Lightly beat the egg and mix with the milk and whisky. Pour into the fruit mixture and mix well. Turn into the pastry case. Turn the edges of the pastry inwards over the top of the filling. Roll out the remaining pastry. Moisten the edges of the pastry and put on the lid. Seal the edges firmly. Prick all over with a fork and glaze with beaten egg. Make several holes in the lid using a skewer, passing the skewer to the bottom of the cake. Bake in a moderate oven (180°C, 350°F, gas mark 4) for 2 -3 hours. If the cake becomes too brown, cover with greaseproof paper. Turn on to a wire rack to cool. Store for several weeks before eating.

# DIET LOAF

| METRIC | IMPERIAL |
|---|---|
| 200 g butter | 8 oz butter |
| 400 g sugar | 1 lb sugar |
| 6 eggs | 6 eggs |
| grated rind of a lemon | grated rind of a lemon |
| $\frac{1}{2}$ teaspoon ground cinnamon | $\frac{1}{2}$ teaspoon ground cinnamon |
| 300 g flour | 12 oz flour |
| icing sugar | icing sugar |

Cream the butter and sugar. Beat the eggs and add to the butter/sugar mixture. Beat well together (20 minutes by hand). Add the grated lemon rind and cinnamon. Gradually stir in the flour, beating well after each addition. Line a baking tin with well greased greaseproof paper and pour in the sponge. Bake in a moderate oven (190°C, 375°F, gas mark 5) for 35 minutes, until the sponge is a pale golden brown. Ice when cold.

# STRAWBERRY SHORTCAKE

| METRIC | IMPERIAL |
|---|---|
| 200 g self raising flour | 8 oz self raising flour |
| pinch of salt | pinch of salt |
| 15 g ground almonds | $\frac{1}{2}$ oz ground almonds |
| 100 g butter | 4 oz butter |
| 50 g sugar | 2 oz sugar |
| 1 egg yolk | 1 egg yolk |
| strawberries and whipping cream | strawberries and whipping cream |

Sift the flour and salt together and mix in the ground almonds. Cream the butter and sugar together until light and fluffy and add the egg yolk. Gradually knead the flour mixture into the butter mixture. Divide into two pieces and roll into rounds 0·75 cm ($\frac{1}{4}$ inch) thick. Place on a greased baking sheet and bake in a moderate oven (180°C, 350°F, gas mark 4) for 30 - 40 minutes until golden brown. Allow to cool. Whip the cream. Hull, wash and dry the strawberries. Cut up half the strawberries and mix with half the cream. Use to sandwich the two cakes together. Pile the remaining cream on top of the cake. Decorate with the rest of the strawberries.

# *SCONES*
## FRUIT SCONES

| METRIC | IMPERIAL |
|---|---|
| *200 g self-raising flour* | *8 oz self-raising flour* |
| *1 teaspoon baking powder* | *1 teaspoon baking powder* |
| *pinch of salt* | *pinch of salt* |
| *50 g butter* | *2 oz butter* |
| *25 g sugar* | *1 oz sugar* |
| *50 g mixed fruit* | *2 oz mixed fruit* |
| *125 ml milk* | *$\frac{1}{4}$ pint milk* |

Sift the dry ingredients together and rub in the butter until the mixture looks like breadcrumbs. Stir in the sugar and fruit. Add enough milk to form a soft dough. Turn on to a floured board and knead lightly. Roll out to a thickness of 2 cm ($\frac{3}{4}$ inches) and cut into 5 cm (2 inch) rounds. Bake on a greased baking sheet in a very hot oven (230°C, 450°F, gas mark 8) for 10 minutes. Serve split and buttered.

## WHOLEMEAL SCONES
Use half wholemeal flour and half plain flour.

## TREACLE SCONES
Add 15 g ($\frac{1}{2}$ oz) sugar, $\frac{1}{2}$ teaspoon each ground cinnamon and mixed spice to the dry ingredients of the scone mixture. Mix 1 tablespoon black treacle with half the milk and add to the mixture. Add the rest of the milk as required.

## GIRDLE SCONES
Make the scone mixture and cook on a fairly hot girdle, allowing 3-4 minutes a side.

# HONEY AND WALNUT SCONES

| METRIC | IMPERIAL |
|---|---|
| *100 g plain wholemeal flour* | *4 oz plain wholemeal flour* |
| *100 g plain white flour* | *4 oz plain white flour* |
| *2 teaspoons baking powder* | *2 teaspoons baking powder* |
| *1 teaspoon ground mixed spice* | *1 teaspoon ground mixed spice* |
| *50 g butter* | *2 oz butter* |
| *1 tablespoon caster sugar* | *1 tablespoon caster sugar* |
| *50 g chopped walnut pieces* | *2 oz chopped walnut pieces* |
| *2 teaspoons lemon juice* | *2 teaspoons lemon juice* |
| *175 ml milk* | *$\frac{1}{3}$ pint milk* |
| *16 walnuts (or 16 halves)* | *16 walnuts (or 16 halves)* |
| *honey* | *honey* |

Sift the flours, baking powder and mixed spice together. Rub in the butter until the mixture looks like breadcrumbs. Stir in the sugar and the chopped walnuts. Mix the lemon juice with the milk and stir into the scone mixture. Turn the dough on to a floured board and knead lightly until it is smooth. Roll out to a 20 cm (8 inch) square. Place on a greased baking sheet and mark into 16 squares. Cut about halfway through the dough. Lightly brush the dough with milk. Place a walnut in each of the squares. Bake in a hot oven (220°C, 425°F, gas mark 7) for 18 minutes until well risen, golden and firm to the touch. Cut into the 16 squares. Serve hot, brushed with a little honey.

# CHEESE SCONES

METRIC
*200 g self-raising flour*
*1 teaspoon baking powder*
*pinch of salt*
*40 g butter*
*100 g grated cheese*
*1 teaspoon mustard*
*250 ml milk*

IMPERIAL
*8 oz self-raising flour*
*1 teaspoon baking powder*
*pinch of salt*
*1 $\frac{1}{2}$ oz butter*
*4 oz grated cheese*
*1 teaspoon mustard*
*$\frac{1}{2}$ pint milk*

Sift the flour, baking powder and salt together. Rub in the butter until the mixture looks like breadcrumbs. Stir in half the cheese and the mustard. Add enough milk to give a fairly soft dough. Roll out on a floured board to a thickness of 2 cm ($\frac{3}{4}$ inch) and cut into 5 cm (2 inch) rounds. Sprinkle with the rest of the cheese. Bake in a hot oven (220°C, 425°F, gas mark 7) for 10 minutes. Serve split and buttered.

# SCOTCH PANCAKES (GRIDDLE SCONES)

METRIC
*100 g self-raising flour*
*pinch of salt*
*25 g sugar*
*1 egg*
*150 ml milk*
*25 g butter (melted)*

IMPERIAL
*4 oz self-raising flour*
*pinch of salt*
*1 oz sugar*
*1 egg*
*$\frac{1}{4}$ pint milk*
*1 oz butter (melted)*

Sift the dry ingredients together. Beat in the egg and then the milk. Mix well. Stir in the melted butter. Drop the mixture in spoonfuls on a hot griddle or electric plate or thick frying pan. Cook for 2 minutes on each side. Serve warm.

## *PASTRIES*

# RASPBERRY TART

| METRIC | IMPERIAL |
|---|---|
| *Shortcrust pastry* | *Shortcrust pastry* |
| *100 g butter* | *4 oz butter* |
| *200 g plain flour* | *8 oz plain flour* |
| *3 tablespoons cold water* | *3 tablespoons cold water* |
| *Filling* | *Filling* |
| *raspberries* | *raspberries* |
| *caster sugar* | *caster sugar* |
| *whipped cream* | *whipped cream* |

Rub the butter into the flour until the mixture looks like breadcrumbs. Add the water and form into a ball. Roll out two thirds of the pastry and line a deep plate. Wash and hull the raspberries and place in the tart. Sprinkle with sugar to taste. Roll out the rest of the pastry to make the lid. Brush with milk and bake in a fairly hot oven ( 200°C, 400°F, gas mark 6) for 25 minutes until the pastry is cooked. Dust with caster sugar and serve with whipped cream.

# FRUIT TARTLETS

Make the shortcrust pastry as above. Cut out bottoms and tops with fluted cutters and line small tartlet tins. Fill with fruit such as apples, blackcurrants, raspberries, redcurrants … Cover with pastry lids and brush with milk. Bake in a fairly hot oven (200°C, 400°F, gas mark 6) for 20 minutes until the pastry is cooked. Dust with caster sugar and serve with whipped cream.

**Open tarts** Bake pastry cases blind. **Fillings:** poached pears, strawberries, raspberries, mandarin oranges … glaze and top with a little whipped cream.

# CARAMELIZED CUSTARD TARTS

| METRIC | IMPERIAL |
|---|---|
| *Pastry* | *Pastry* |
| 150 g flour | 6 oz flour |
| pinch of salt | pinch of salt |
| 100 g butter | 4 oz butter |
| 50 g caster sugar | 2 oz caster sugar |
| white of 1 egg | white of 1 egg |
| *Filling* | *Filling* |
| 1 large egg + 1 yolk | 1 large egg + 1 yolk |
| 25 g caster sugar | 1 oz caster sugar |
| 250 ml milk | $\frac{1}{2}$ pint milk |
| 100 g raspberries | 4 oz raspberries |
| *Topping* | *Topping* |
| 50 g light brown sugar | 2 oz light brown sugar |
| few strawberries | few strawberries |

**Pastry** Sift the flour and salt. Rub the butter into the flour until the mixture looks like breadcrumbs. Stir in the sugar and egg white to make a firm dough. Roll out thinly and use to line six fairly deep patty tins. Bake in the centre of a hot oven (220°C, 425°F, gas mark 7) for ten minutes. Take the pastry cases out of the oven and leave to cool for a few minutes. Reduce the temperature of the oven to 180°C, 350°F, gas mark 4.

**Filling** Mix the large egg and the yolk with the sugar. Heat the milk but do not let it boil. Stir it into the egg mixture. Rinse the milk pan and return the custard to the pan. Cook gently until the mixture thickens (coats the back of a spoon). Do not boil. Place the raspberries in the bottom of the pastry cases. Pour over the custard. Bake the tarts in the centre of the oven at 180°C, 350°F, gas mark 4 for 15 - 20 minutes until the custard sets.

**Topping** Before serving, sprinkle the brown sugar over the surface of the custard tarts. Place the tarts under a hot grill for 1 minute to caramelize the sugar. Decorate with strawberries.

# RASPBERRY DRAMBUIE OATY CRUMBLE

METRIC
*800 g raspberries*
*60 ml Drambuie*
*50 g light brown soft sugar*
**Topping**
*100 g unsalted butter (diced)*
*100 g plain wholemeal flour*
*50 g shelled hazlenuts (chopped)*
*150 g porridge oats*
*100 g light brown soft sugar*
*½ teaspoon ground cinnamon*
*120 ml sunflower oil*

IMPERIAL
*2 lb raspberries*
*4 tablespoons Drambuie*
*2 oz light brown soft sugar*
**Topping**
*4 oz unsalted butter (diced)*
*4 oz plain wholemeal flour*
*2 oz shelled hazlenuts (chopped)*
*6 oz porridge oats*
*4 oz light brown soft sugar*
*½ teaspoon ground cinnamon*
*⅓ pint sunflower oil*

Place the raspberries in an ovenproof dish, capacity 2•25 litres (4 pints) and sprinkle over the Drambuie and sugar.

**Topping** Rub the butter into the flour and stir in the chopped nuts, oats, sugar and cinnamon. Add the sunflower oil and combine to a crumbly mixture. Spread the mixture over the raspberries. Bake in a moderately hot oven (190°C, 375°F, gas mark 5) for 45 - 50 minutes until golden brown on top.

# TRIFLES AND CREAMS
## SCOTCH TRIFLE

| METRIC | IMPERIAL |
|---|---|
| *Custard* | *Custard* |
| 2 eggs | 2 eggs |
| 250 ml milk | ½ pint milk |
| vanilla essence | vanilla essence |
| 25 g sugar | 1 oz sugar |
| *Trifle* | *Trifle* |
| 4 small trifle sponges | 4 small trifle sponges |
| raspberry jam | raspberry jam |
| 25 g ratafias | 1 oz ratafias |
| 6 macaroons | 6 macaroons |
| 200 g raspberries (or a can of sliced peaches) | 8 oz raspberries (or a can of sliced peaches) |
| 6 tablespoons sherry or brandy and water | 6 tablespoons sherry or brandy and water |
| ½ teaspoon vanilla essence | ½ teaspoon vanilla essence |
| 250 ml custard | ½ pint custard |
| 250 ml cream | ½ pint cream |
| 2 teaspoons caster sugar | 2 teaspoons caster sugar |
| 25 g almonds | 1 oz almonds |

**Custard:** Lightly beat the eggs. Heat the milk but do not boil. Pour over the beaten eggs. Strain. Warm over a low heat, with constant stirring, until the custard thickens. Do not boil. Add the vanilla essence and sugar and stir.

**Trifle:** Slice the sponges and spread with jam. Place at the bottom of a trifle bowl. Add the ratafias, macaroons and fruit keeping a little fruit for decoration. Pour the sherry or brandy and water and vanilla essence over the mixture. When the custard is cool, pour into the bowl. Whip the cream and sugar and pile on top. Decorate with almonds and raspberries or slices of peach.

# TIPSY LAIRD

METRIC
*15 g butter*
*50 g blanched almonds*
*25 g sugar*
*30 trifle fingers*
*150 ml sherry*
*4 tablespoons brandy*
*finely grated rind and juice of 1 large orange*
*250 ml whipping cream*
*250 g natural yogurt*

IMPERIAL
*$\frac{1}{2}$ oz butter*
*2 oz blanched almonds*
*1 oz sugar*
*30 trifle fingers*
*$\frac{1}{4}$ pint sherry*
*4 tablespoons brandy*
*finely grated rind and juice of 1 large orange*
*$\frac{1}{2}$ pint whipping cream*
*10 oz natural yogurt*

Melt the butter in a heavy-based frying pan and fry the almonds until golden brown. Stir in the sugar and cook for 1 minute. Stir continuously until the sugar dissolves and the almonds are well coated. Turn on to a greased baking sheet and leave to cool. About 30 minutes before serving, break the sponge cakes in half and place in a serving bowl. Pour the sherry, brandy, grated orange rind and juice over the sponges and leave to soak for 30 minutes. Whip the cream until it just holds its shape. Fold in the yogurt. Spoon the cream mixture on top of the sponges. Roughly chop the almonds, sprinkle on top of the cream and serve immediately. [Use fresh fruit juice instead of the sherry and brandy if preferred.]

# PRINCE CHARLIE'S SOUFFLE

| METRIC | IMPERIAL |
|--------|----------|
| 25 g butter | 1 oz butter |
| 25 g flour | 1 oz flour |
| 125 ml milk | $\frac{1}{4}$ pint milk |
| 25 g caster sugar | 1 oz caster sugar |
| 2 tablespoons Drambuie | 2 tablespoons Drambuie |
| 3 egg yolks | 3 egg yolks |
| 4 egg whites (beaten) | 4 egg whites (beaten) |
| 400 g raspberries | 1 lb raspberries |
| whipped cream | whipped cream |

Melt the butter over a low heat and blend in the flour. Cook for a minute. Remove from the heat and gradually beat in the milk. Add the sugar and heat until the mixture leaves the sides of the pan. Leave to cool for a few minutes and then add the Drambuie. Beat the egg yolks into the mixture, one at a time. Fold in the egg whites. Pour into a greased soufflé dish and bake in the centre of a fairly hot oven (190°C, 375°F, gas mark 5) for 35 minutes. Serve at once with raspberries and cream.

# FRUIT FOOL

| METRIC | IMPERIAL |
|--------|----------|
| 150 ml double cream | $\frac{1}{4}$ pint double cream |
| 450 ml fruit purée, sweetened to taste | $\frac{2}{3}$ pint fruit purée, sweetened to taste |
| sponge fingers | sponge fingers |

Whip the cream and fold into the fruit. Pile into individual serving dishes. Chill and serve with sponge fingers. Use fresh or canned strawberries, raspberries, rhubarb, apricots, blackcurrants or gooseberries. Simmer fruit in water to soften if necessary, drain and cool.

# RASPBERRY MOUSSE

| METRIC | IMPERIAL |
| --- | --- |
| 400 g fresh raspberries | 1 lb fresh raspberries |
| caster sugar to taste | caster sugar to taste |
| 150 ml whipping cream | $\frac{1}{4}$ pint whipping cream |
| 4 teaspoons gelatine | 4 teaspoons gelatine |
| 3 tablespoons water | 3 tablespoons water |
| 2 egg whites (whisked) | 2 egg whites (whisked) |
| whipped cream and raspberries for decoration | whipped cream and raspberries for decoration |

Purée the raspberry and sieve. Whip the cream until it just holds its shape. Mix the fruit, sugar and cream. Put the gelatine and the water in a basin standing in a pan of hot water. Heat gently until the gelatine dissolves. Allow to cool slightly. Pour slowly into the raspberry mixture, stirring all the time. Fold in the whisked egg whites. Pour into a dish and leave in a cool place to set. Decorate with whipped cream and raspberries.

# CHOCOLATE CREAMS

| METRIC | IMPERIAL |
| --- | --- |
| 3 eggs (separated) | 3 eggs (separated) |
| 100 g plain chocolate | 4 oz plain chocolate |
| 75 g unsalted butter | 3 oz unsalted butter |
| 75 g caster sugar | 3 oz caster sugar |
| orange rind (grated) | orange rind (grated) |
| 150 ml whipped cream | $\frac{1}{4}$ pint whipped cream |

Break the chocolate into small pieces and melt in a basin standing in hot water. Remove from the heat and stir in the butter and sugar. Add the egg yolks, beating well after each has been added. Add the grated orange rind, keeping some for decoration. Whisk the egg whites until they form stiff peaks. Fold into the chocolate mixture and pour into little soufflé dishes. Chill. Serve decorated with whipped cream and grated orange rind.

# CRUMPETS AND MUFFINS
## SCOTS CRUMPETS

METRIC
*100 g self-raising flour*
*15 g caster sugar*
*15 g butter*
*2 eggs*
*125 ml milk*

IMPERIAL
*4 oz self-raising flour*
*½ oz caster sugar*
*½ oz butter*
*2 eggs*
*¼ pint milk*

Mix the flour and sugar together. Rub in the butter. Lightly beat the egs. Mix the eggs and milk with the flour mixture, keeping the batter smooth. Drop spoonfuls on to a hot girdle. When brown on one side, turn and cook on the other side. Cool in a towel.

## MUFFINS

METRIC
*15 g fresh yeast or 7 g dried yeast*
*1 teaspoon sugar*
*300 ml warm water*
*200 g flour*
*1 teaspoon salt*

IMPERIAL
*½ oz fresh yeast or ¼ oz dried yeast*
*1 teaspoon sugar*
*½ pint warm wter*
*8 oz flour*
*1 teaspoon salt*

Dissolve the sugar in the water and add the yeast. Stir and leave to stand for 10 minutes until the mixture is frothy. Sift the flour and salt together. Make a well in the middle of the flour and pour in the yeast liquid. Draw in the flour and mix to a smooth dough. Knead for about 10 minutes until the dough is smooth. Place in a bowl, cover with a tea-towel and leave in a warm place for about an hour until double in size. Roll out to a thickness of of 1 cm (½ inch). Cover with a tea towel and leave for 5 minutes. Cut into rounds using a 7•5 (3 inch) cutter. Cook on a greased griddle, electric griddle plate or heavy frying pan for about 6 minutes on each side. To serve, pull apart (not cut) and butter.
**Fruit or Nut Muffins** Stir 50 g (2 oz) sugar and 75 g (3 oz) dried fruit or 50 g (2 oz) chopped nuts into the flour/salt mixture. **Wholemeal Muffins** Replace half the flour by wholemeal flour.

# SANDWICHES

Use brown and white bread and rolls. Soften the butter to make spreading easier. Fillings should be tasty. Wrap sandwiches in foil or polythene and keep in a refrigerator. Avoid over-moist fillings which make the bread soggy.

## Savoury and Sweet Butters

Cream butter with any of the following:
*cooked prawns, lemon juice and pepper*
*cream cheese and chopped watercress*
*cream cheese, crushed walnuts*
*\*brown sugar, rum, orange juice*
*\*caster sugar, brandy, lemon juice*
*sardines, Worcester sauce, salt and pepper*
*anchovy fillets, lemon juice*
*mixed herbs*

*\*Use unsalted butter*

## Sweet fillings

*Jams*
*Chopped dates and chopped sweet apple*
*Honey and banana*
*Lemon curd and chopped sweet apple*
*Chopped nuts and honey*
*Cream cheese with strawberry jam*
*Sliced banana with raspberry jam*
*Sliced banana and marmalade*

## Savoury fillings

*Minced cooked beef and horseradish sauce*
*Ham, chopped chives (or onions) and mustard*
*Tongue and chopped tomato*
*Corned beef, lettuce and mayonnaise*
*Chicken and salad*
*Lettuce and tomato*
*Cream cheese and watercress*
*Grated cheese and pickle*
*Sardines (skinned, boned and mashed)*
*with a squeeze of lemon juice*
*Tongue and cucumber*
*Grated cheese and onion*
*Cucumber and chives*
*Mashed egg and chopped chives*
*Meat pâté and sliced cucumber*
*Chopped cooked bacon and mushrooms*
*Poached salmon and thinly sliced cucumber*
*Chopped apple and chutney*
*Cream cheese, apple chutney and chopped nuts*
*Smoked salmon, cream, whisky and grated nutmeg*
*Prawns, mayonnaise and watercress*

# SAVOURIES

## CHICKEN PANCAKES AND WHISKY SAUCE

| METRIC | IMPERIAL |
|---|---|
| ***Pancakes:*** | ***Pancakes:*** |
| *100 g plain flour* | *4 oz plain flour* |
| *pinch of salt* | *pinch of salt* |
| *1 egg* | *1 egg* |
| *250 ml milk* | *½ pint milk* |
| *fat for frying* | *fat for frying* |
| ***Filling:*** | ***Filling:*** |
| *15 g butter* | *½ oz butter* |
| *25 g flour* | *1 oz flour* |
| *500 ml milk* | *1 pint milk* |
| *200 g cooked chicken* | *8 oz cooked chicken* |
| *100 g mushrooms* | *4 oz mushrooms* |
| *3 tablespoons whisky* | *3 tablespoons whisky* |
| *2 teaspoons chopped parsley* | *2 teaspoons chopped parsley* |
| *salt and pepper* | *salt and pepper* |

**Pancakes:** Sift the flour and salt together. Add the egg and a little milk to the flour. Mix well, avoiding the formation of lumps. Stir in the rest of the milk and beat until smooth. Cover and leave to stand for 1 hour. Coat a frying pan with fat and heat until hot. Pour a little of the batter into the frying pan, tilting the pan so that the base of the pan is thinly covered. When cooked on one side, turn over. Keep the pancakes warm.

**Filling:** Melt the butter and work in the flour to make a smooth paste. Slowly add the milk, stirring to avoid the formation of lumps. Heat gently until the sauce thickens and cook for 3 minutes. Cut up the chicken and mushrooms and add to the sauce. Season and simmer until the mushrooms are cooked. Add the whisky and chopped parsley. Place a little in the centre of each pancake and roll up. Serve hot.

# GALANTINE OF VENISON AND PORK

METRIC
*1•2 kg thick breast venison*
*2 litres water*
*sprig of thyme and marjoram*
*6 black peppercorns*
*200 g ham*
*400 g minced pork or sausage meat*
*3 cloves garlic (crushed, optional)*
*3 eggs*
*salt and pepper*

IMPERIAL
*3 lb thick breast venison*
*4 pints water*
*sprig of thyme and marjoram*
*6 black peppercorns*
*8 oz ham*
*1 lb minced pork or sausage meat*
*3 cloves garlic (crushed, optional)*
*3 eggs*
*salt and pepper*

Bone the venison and remove any gristle. Boil the venison bones with the water, seasoned with the herbs and salt. Cut the ham into small pieces and mix with the minced pork or sausage meat and garlic to taste. Hard boil the eggs and cut in half. Lay the boned venison on a board. Cover with half the minced pork or sausage meat mixture, add the eggs and then the rest of the meat mixture. Season. Roll up the venison and put in a floured cloth. Remove the bones from the stock. Place the venison in its cloth in the stock. Cover and simmer for 4 hours. Top up with water if necessary. Leave to cool in the water. When cold, remove from the stock and place in a dish that just fits it. Cover with foil and put a weight on top. Leave in the refrigerator overnight. Serve cold, sliced, with a green salad.

# DUMFRIES PIE

METRIC
*shortcrust pastry*
*75 g bacon*
*1 tomato*
*2 eggs*
*salt and pepper*

IMPERIAL
*shortcrust pastry*
*3 oz bacon*
*1 tomato*
*2 eggs*
*salt and pepper*

Make shortcrust pastry as on page 18. Using half the pastry line a flan tin or deep pie plate. Cut up the bacon. Place the tomato in boiling water. Skin and cut up. Mix with the bacon pieces aand spread over the flan case. Lightly beat the eggs. Season and pour over the bacon mixture. Cover with the rest of the pastry. Brush with a little milk. Bake in a fairly hot oven (200°C, 400°F, gas mark 6) for 20-25 minutes.

# SAUSAGE ROLLS

METRIC
*shortcrust pastry*
*200 g sausage meat*
*flour*
*milk to glaze*

IMPERIAL
*shortcrust pastry*
*8 oz sausage meat*
*flour*
*milk to glaze*

Make the shortcrust pastry as on page 18. Roll the pastry into an oblong and divide in two lengthwise. Divide the sausage meat in two and form into 2 rolls each the length of the pastry. Dust with flour and place on the pastry. Roll each strip over to enclose the sausage, closing the seam by flaking or scalloping. Brush with milk and cut into pieces 5 cm (2 inches) long. Place on a baking sheet and bake in a fairly hot oven ( 204°C, 400°F, gas mark 6) for 15 minutes and then in a slightly cooler oven (180°C, 350°F, gas mark 4) for a further 15 minutes to cook the sausage meat.

# HOTWATER CRUST PASTRY

| METRIC | IMPERIAL |
|---|---|
| *300 g flour* | *12 oz flour* |
| *1 teaspoon salt* | *1 teaspoon salt* |
| *100 g lard or cooking fat* | *4 oz lard or cooking fat* |
| *125 ml water or milk and water* | *¼ pint water or milk and water* |

Sift the flour and salt together. Melt the fat in the liquid and bring to the boil. Pour into a well in the flour mixture and stir. Work into a lump using a wooden spoon. Knead lightly until smooth. Place in a plastic bag or cover with a damp cloth and stand in a warm place for 30 minutes.

# VEAL AND HAM PIE

| METRIC | IMPERIAL |
|---|---|
| *hotwater crust pastry* | *hotwater crust pastry* |
| *100 g ham* | *4 oz ham* |
| *400 g shoulder of veal* | *1 lb shoulder of veal* |
| *pinch mixed herbs* | *pinch mixed herbs* |
| *pinch ground mace* | *pinch ground mace* |
| *salt and pepper* | *salt and pepper* |
| *2 hard boiled eggs* | *2 hard boiled eggs* |
| *beaten egg or milk to glaze* | *beaten egg or milk to glaze* |
| *2 teaspoons gelatine* | *2 teaspoons gelatine* |
| *250 ml chicken stock* | *½ pint chicken stock* |
| *4 tablespoons water or stock* | *4 tablespoons water or stock* |

Roll out two thirds of the pastry on a floured board, keeping the remainder warm and covered until ready for use. Lift on to the outside of a pie dish and mould into a pie-shape. Carefully remove the pie dish and place the pastry shell on to a greased baking sheet. Cut the meat into small pieces and mix with the herbs and seasoning. Fill the pastry shell with the meat mixture, placing the eggs in the middle. Wet the edges of the pie. Roll out the rest of the pastry to make a lid. Seal the edges and brush the lid with beaten egg or milk. Tie a piece of greaseproof paper around the pie. Cook in a fairly hot oven (220°C, 425°F, gas mark 7) for 20 minutes. Cook for a further 2 hours at a slightly lower temperature (180°C, 350°F, gas mark 4) until the meat is cooked and feels tender when tested with a skewer. Dissolve the gelatine in the stock. When the pie is cold, make two small holes in the lid and pour in the jelly stock. Leave to set.

### *To make 4 small pies:*
Use jam jars as pie moulds and cook for a total of 1 hour or until the meat is tender.

# GLAZED BAKED HAM

| METRIC | IMPERIAL |
|---|---|
| *2 kg gammon* | *5 lb gammon* |
| *3 tablespoons clear honey* | *3 tablespoons clear honey* |
| *1 tablespoon grated orange peel* | *1 tablespoon grated orange peel* |

Wash the ham and soak for 2 hours. Dry and wrap in aluminium cooking foil. Bake in a fairly hot oven (190°C, 375°F, gas mark 5) for 3-3½ hours. 30 minutes before the ham is cooked, score the fat of the ham into diamond shapes. Mix the honey and orange peel and coat the ham. Return to the oven and complete baking. Serve with salad.

# KINGDOM OF FIFE PIE

| METRIC | IMPERIAL |
|---|---|
| *1 rabbit* | *1 rabbit* |
| *200 g pork* | *8 oz pork* |
| *1 egg* | *1 egg* |
| *300 ml beef stock* | *½ pint beef stock* |
| *forcemeat balls* | *forcemeat balls* |
| *salt and pepper* | *salt and pepper* |
| ***Forcemeat*** | ***Forcemeat*** |
| *1 rabbit liver* | *1 rabbit liver* |
| *1 rasher bacon* | *1 rasher bacon* |
| *100 g breadcrumbs* | *4 oz breadcrumbs* |
| *1 tablespoon thyme* | *1 tablespoon thyme* |
| *milk* | *milk* |

Skin and clean the rabbit, keeping the liver aside. Divide into joints. Dice the pork. Hard boil the egg and slice. Place the rabbit, pork, egg and forcemeat balls in a pie dish. Add the stock. Season. Cover with rough puff pastry. Cook in a hot oven (230°C, 450°F, gas mark 8) for 30 minutes until the pastry is risen and golden brown and then in a warm oven (170°C, 325°F, gas mark 3) for 40 minutes until the meat is tender when tested with a skewer.

**Forcemeat balls**  Simmer the liver in salted water for 10 minutes. Mince the liver and chop up the bacon. Mix all the ingredients together and bind with a little milk.

# FORFAR BRIDIES

METRIC
*Shortcrust pastry (See page 18, use double quantities)*
*400 g minced beef*
*1 large onion*
*salt and pepper*

IMPERIAL
*Shortcrust pastry (See page 18, use double quantities)*
*1 lb minced beef*
*1 large onion*
*salt and pepper*

Skin and dice the onion and mix with the beef. Season. Roll out the pastry to make eight ovals. Cover half of each oval with the meat mixture and damp the edges of the pastry. Fold over and crimp the pastry edges together . Make two small holes in the top of each. Bake for 30 minutes in a hot oven (230ºC, 450ºF, gas mark 8) and then at 200ºC, 400ºF, gas mark 6 for 30 minutes until the meat is cooked.

# ORKNEY CHEESE

METRIC
*4 litres milk*
*1 teaspoon rennet*
*½ teaspoon salt*
*oatmeal to store*

IMPERIAL
*8 pints milk*
*1 teaspoon rennet*
*½ teaspoon salt*
*oatmeal to store*

Heat the milk to 29ºC, 85ºF.  Add the rennet and a little water.  Stir with a wooden spoon for 5 minutes.  Leave to stand for 30 minutes to form a smooth curd.  Cut the curd in several directions using a bread knife.  Let it stand for 15 minutes.  Stir and strain through a cheese cloth.  Break up the curd with the hand and mix in the salt.  Place in a cheese cog or chessel with the cloth underneath.  Cover the top with the cloth, replace the lid and put a 7lb weight on it.  Leave for 8 days, changing the cloth each day and increasing the weights if necessary.  When dry, store in oatmeal.

# CHEESE LOAF

METRIC
*200 g self raising flour*
*½ teaspoon dry mustard*
*½ teaspoon onion salt*
*pinch cayenne pepper*
*50 g butter*
*100 g Cheddar cheese*
*1 egg*
*milk*

IMPERIAL
*8 oz self raising flour*
*½ teaspoon dry mustard*
*½ teaspoon onion salt*
*pinch cayenne pepper*
*2 oz butter*
*4 oz Cheddar cheese*
*1 egg*
*milk*

Sift the dry ingredients together (except the cheese). Rub in the butter until the mixture looks like breadcrumbs. Grate the cheese and stir into the mixture. Lightly beat the egg and add enough milk to the beaten egg to make 125 ml (¼ pint). Add to the flour and cheese mixture and mix to form a firm dough. Turn on to a lightly floured board. Knead until smooth. Place in a greased 1 kg (2 lb) loaf tin. Bake in a moderate oven (190°C, 375°F, gas mark 5) for 40 minutes until the loaf sounds hollow when tapped.

# CHEESE POTATO CAKES

METRIC
*15 g butter*
*200 g hot, boiled, mashed potatoes*
*50 g flour*
*100 g grated cheese*
*2 eggs*
*50 g breadcrumbs*
*fat for frying*

IMPERIAL
*½ oz butter*
*8 oz hot, boiled, mashed potatoes*
*2 oz flour*
*4 oz grated cheese*
*2 eggs*
*2 oz breadcrumbs*
*fat for frying*

Add the butter to the potatoes. Work the flour into the potatoes and add the cheese. Beat the eggs and add to the mixture. Shape into round cakes, dip into breadcrumbs and fry in hot fat.

# POTTED SHRIMPS

| METRIC | IMPERIAL |
|---|---|
| *50 g butter* | *2 oz butter* |
| *100 g shrimps (cooked or frozen)* | *4 oz shrimps (cooked or frozen)* |
| *pinch ground mace* | *pinch ground mace* |
| *pinch ground nutmeg* | *pinch ground nutmeg* |
| *salt and pepper* | *salt and pepper* |

Melt half the butter in a pan and add the shrimps. Season. Heat for 2-3 minutes. Sieve or gently mash. Spoon into sterilized jars. Melt the rest of the butter and pour over the top of the shrimps.

# POTTED BEEF

| METRIC | IMPERIAL |
|---|---|
| *400 g stewing steak* | *1 lb stewing steak* |
| *125 ml stock or water* | *¼ pint stock or water* |
| *1 clove* | *1 clove* |
| *1 blade mace* | *1 blade mace* |
| *salt and pepper* | *salt and pepper* |
| *50 g butter* | *2 oz butter* |

Remove the skin and as much fat as possible from the meat. Cut the meat into cubes. Place in an ovenproof dish with the stock or water, clove and mace. Season. Cook for $1\frac{1}{2}$ - 2 hours in a moderate oven (180°C, 350°F, gas mark 4). Drain the liquid, remove the clove and finely mince the meat (or blend the meat in an electric blender). Melt the butter and mix half into the beef. Spoon into sterilized jars and seal with the rest of the melted butter. Keep in a refrigerator and use within 2 days. Serve on toast or brown bread.

# PLAIN OMELETTE

METRIC
*2 eggs*
*salt and pepper*
*1 tablespoon cold water*
*nub of butter*

IMPERIAL
*2 eggs*
*salt and pepper*
*1 tablespoon cold water*
*nub of butter*

Whisk the eggs but do not overbeat or make frothy. Season and add the cold water. Lightly grease the omelette pan with the butter and place over a gentle heat. When the pan is hot pour the egg mixture into the hot fat. Stir until the egg mixture sets. Cook for 1 more minute. Turn the top third of the omelette towards the centre and then turn the bottom third towards the centre. Turn on to a hot plate and serve at once.

# CHEESE OMELETTE

Grate 25 g (1oz) cheese. Place half of this in the centre of the omelette before folding. Sprinkle the rest of the cheese over the omelette after folding.

# KIDNEY OMELETTE

Skin, core and chop 1 sheep's kidney. Add 1 teaspoon of chopped onion and fry in butter until tender. Place in the centre of the omelette before folding.

# SHRIMP OMELETTE

Gently sauté 50 g (2 oz) shrimps in butter and place in the centre of the omelette before folding. Serve at once with a squeeze of lemon juice.

## *BISCUITS*

# SHORTBREAD

| METRIC | IMPERIAL |
|--------|----------|
| *200 g flour* | *8 oz flour* |
| *50 g caster sugar* | *2 oz caster sugar* |
| *100 g butter* | *4 oz butter* |

Mix the flour and sugar and rub into the butter. Knead well. Roll out and cut into strips. Prick all over. Bake in a moderate oven (180ºC, 350ºF, gas mark 4) for 30-40 minutes until lightly browned. Cut into biscuits before cold.

# GINGER SHORTBREAD

Add $\frac{1}{2}$ teaspoon ground ginger to the flour in the recipe for shortbread.

# RAISIN SHORTBREAD

| METRIC | IMPERIAL |
|--------|----------|
| *100 g butter* | *4 oz butter* |
| *50 g caster sugar* | *2 oz caster sugar* |
| *200 g flour* | *8 oz flour* |
| *100 g raisins* | *4 oz raisins* |

Cream the butter and sugar together. Work in the flour to make a firm dough. Divide in half. Roll out each piece into a rectangle of 0•75 cm thickness ( $\frac{1}{4}$ inch). Spread the raisins over one piece and place the other piece on top. Press together and pinch the edges. Prick well. Bake for 45 minutes at 180ºC, 350ºF, gas mark 4). Cut into pieces when cool.

# OATY PIECES

| METRIC | IMPERIAL |
| --- | --- |
| 100 g self-raising flour | 4 oz self-raising flour |
| 100 g fine oatmeal | 4 oz fine oatmeal |
| 125 ml corn oil | $\frac{1}{4}$ pint corn oil |
| 100 g black treacle | 4 oz black treacle |
| 25 g sugar | 1 oz sugar |
| 1 egg | 1 egg |
| 4 tablespoons milk | 4 tablespoons milk |

Grease and line an 18 cm (7 inch) square tin. Mix the flour and oatmeal together in a basin. Gently warm the corn oil, treacle and sugar in a saucepan until the sugar dissolves. Beat the egg lightly with the milk. Make a hole in the oatmeal mixture and pour in the sugar and egg liquids. Beat well. Pour into the tin and bake for $1-1\frac{1}{2}$ hours in a warm oven (170°C, 325°F, gas mark 3). Turn on to a wire rack to cool. This is best left for a day or two before being cut into pieces.

# ABERNETHY BISCUITS

| METRIC | IMPERIAL |
| --- | --- |
| 200 g flour | 8 oz flour |
| 1 teaspoon cream of tartar | 1 teaspoon cream of tartar |
| 1 teaspoon bicarbonate of soda | 1 teaspoon bicarbonate of soda |
| 100 g butter | 4 oz butter |
| 50 g caster sugar | 2 oz caster sugar |
| 1 teaspoon milk | 1 teaspoon milk |
| pinch of salt | pinch of salt |

Sift the flour, cream of tartar and bicarbonate of soda together. Rub in the butter until the mixture looks like breadcrumbs. Melt the sugar in the milk and stir into the fat mixture. Form into a stiff dough and roll out to a thickness of 0•5 cm ($\frac{1}{4}$ inch). Cut into biscuit shapes. Prick with a fork and bake on a baking sheet in a moderate oven (180°C, 350°F, gas mark 4) for 20 minutes.

# BREAD AND TEABREADS

## SCOTCH OATMEAL BREAD

| METRIC | IMPERIAL |
|---|---|
| 2 eggs | 2 eggs |
| 200 g sugar | 8 oz sugar |
| 375 ml sour milk or buttermilk | $\frac{3}{4}$ pint sour milk or buttermilk |
| 200 g treacle | 8 oz treacle |
| 300 g flour | 12 oz flour |
| 1 teaspoon baking powder | 1 teaspoon baking powder |
| 2 teaspoons bicarbonate of soda | 2 teaspoons bicarbonate of soda |
| 150 g oatmeal | 6 oz oatmeal |
| 50 g chopped nuts | 2 oz chopped nuts |
| 250 g raisins | 9 oz raisins |
| 1 teaspoon salt | 1 teaspoons salt |

Lightly beat the eggs. Add the sugar and beat until the mixture is fluffy. Add the sour milk and treacle. Mix thoroughly. Sift the flour, salt, baking powder and bicarbonate of soda together. Fold into the sour milk mixture. Fold in the remaining ingredients - the oatmeal, nuts and raisins. Line two bread tins, 11 cm x 21 cm (5 inches x 8 inches) with greased greaseproof paper. Turn the mixture into the tins and bake in a moderate oven (180°C, 350°F, gas mark 4) for 1 hour. Leave for 1 day before eating.

# SELKIRK BANNOCK

METRIC
*200 g butter*
*250 ml warm milk*
*25 g fresh yeast or 15 g dried yeast*
*800 g flour*
*200 g sugar*
*400 g sultanas or seedless raisins*
*100 g chopped candied orange peel (optional)*
*milk and sugar for glazing*

IMPERIAL
*8 oz butter*
*½ pint warm milk*
*1 oz fresh yeast or ½ oz dried yeast*
*2 lb flour*
*8 oz sugar*
*1 lb sultanas or seedless raisins*
*4 oz chopped candied orange peel (optional)*
*milk and sugar for glazing*

Melt the butter until it is soft but not oily. Add to the warm milk. Cream the yeast with 1 teaspoon sugar and add to the milk and butter mixture. Sift the flour into a bowl and make a well in the middle. Pour the liquid into the well. Draw in the flour to make a smooth dough. Cover with a cloth and leave in a warm place for about 1 hour until it has doubled in size. Knead well. Work in the fruit and remaining sugar. Form into a flat round or place in a greased loaf tin. Cover and again leave in a warm place for ¾ hour. Bake in a moderate oven (180°C, 350°F, gas mark 4) for 1 - 1½ hours. Half an hour before it is cooked, remove from the oven and glaze with warm milk containing a little sugar. When cooked, the loaf sounds hollow when tapped.

# MARMALADE TEABREAD

METRIC
*200 g plain flour*
*1 teaspoon ground ginger*
*1 teaspoon baking powder*
*50 g butter*
*50 g light soft brown sugar*
*4 tablespoons orange marmalade*

IMPERIAL
*8 oz plain flour*
*1 teaspoon ground ginger*
*1 teaspoon baking powder*
*2 oz butter*
*2 oz light soft brown sugar*
*4 tablespoons orange marmalade*

| | |
|---|---|
| *1 egg (beaten)* | *1 egg (beaten)* |
| *3 tablespoons milk* | *3 tablespoons milk* |
| *25 g candied orange peel (chopped)* | *1 oz candied orange peel (chopped)* |

Grease a 750 ml (1½ pint) loaf tin and line it with greased greaseproof paper. Sift the flour, ginger and baking powder together. Rub in the butter until the mixture looks like breadcrumbs. Stir in the sugar. Mix together the marmalade, egg and most of the milk. Stir into the dry ingredients and mix to a soft dough. Add the rest of the milk, if necessary. Turn the mixture into the prepared tin. Level the surface and press the candied orange peel on top. Bake in a moderate oven (170°C, 325°F, gas mark 3) for 1¼ hours until golden brown. Turn out on a wire rack to cool.

# MALTED FRUIT TEABREAD

| METRIC | IMPERIAL |
|---|---|
| *200 g self-raising flour* | *8 oz self-raising flour* |
| *pinch of salt* | *pinch of salt* |
| *2 tablespoons dark, soft, brown sugar* | *2 tablespoons dark, soft, brown sugar* |
| *150 g mixed, dried fruit* | *6 oz mixed, dried fruit* |
| *2 tablespoons golden syrup* | *2 tablespoons golden syrup* |
| *2 tablespoons malt extract* | *2 tablespoons malt extract* |
| *150 ml milk* | *¼ pint* |

Grease a 900 ml (2 pint) loaf tin and line with greased greaseproof paper. Mix the flour, salt, sugar and fruit together. Make a well in the centre. Put the syrup, malt extract and milk in a saucepan and heat gently until melted. Make a well in the centre of the dry ingredients. Pour the syrup mixture into the well. Beat together thoroughly. Add a little extra milk, if necessary, to make a fairly sticky consistency. Turn the mixture into the prepared tin and bake in a moderate oven (170°C, 325°F, gas mark 3) for about 1¼ hours. Turn out and leave to cool on a wire rack. When cool, wrap in greaseproof paper and foil and store for 1 day before eating. Serve sliced, spread with butter.

# *SWEETS*

## RASPBERRY CHEESE

| METRIC | IMPERIAL |
|---|---|
| *200 g grated Orkney Cheese* | *8 oz grated Orkney cheese* |
| *75 g caster sugar* | *3 oz caster sugar* |
| *400 g raspberries* | *1 lb raspberries* |
| *1 teaspoon lemon juice* | *1 teaspoon lemon juice* |
| *wafers* | *wafers* |

Whisk grated cheese, sugar, raspberries and lemon juice together. Put into individual dishes. Chill. Serve decorated with a few raspberries and wafers.

## ORANGES 'N WHISKY

| METRIC | IMPERIAL |
|---|---|
| *4 oranges* | *4 oranges* |
| *2 tablespoons demerara sugar* | *2 tablespoons demerara sugar* |
| *3 tablespoons water* | *3 tablespoons water* |
| *3 tablespoons malt whisky* | *3 tablespoons malt whisky* |
| *whipped cream* | *whipped cream* |

Peel and thinly slice 3 oranges removing all pips and pith. Put the juice from the remaining orange with the sugar, whisky and water in a pan. Heat gently until the sugar dissolves. Simmer for 2 minutes. Add orange slices and raise the heat for 1 - 2 minutes. Remove from the heat. Arrange the fruit in a dish. Pour over the pan juices and chill. Serve with whipped cream.

# RASPBERRIES IN WHITE PORT

| METRIC | IMPERIAL |
|---|---|
| 1 kg raspberries | 2 lb raspberries |
| 75 g caster sugar | 3 oz caster sugar |
| 5 tablespoons orange Curaçao | 5 tablespoons orange Curaçao |
| 125 ml white port | ¼ pint white port |
| cream | cream |

Put the fruit and sugar in layers in a bowl. Pour over the Curaçao and leave to stand for 30 minutes then pour over the white port. Chill well. Serve with cream.

# BUTTERSCOTCH SAUCE

| METRIC | IMPERIAL |
|---|---|
| *50 g butter* | *2 oz butter* |
| *2 tablespoons cold water* | *2 tablespoons cold water* |
| *75 g brown sugar* | *3 oz brown sugar* |
| *1 egg yolk (beaten)* | *1 egg yolk (beaten)* |
| *4 tablespoons thick cream (whipped)* | *4 tablespoons thick cream (whipped)* |
| *2 drops vanilla essence* | *2 drops vanilla essence* |

Melt the butter over a low heat and add the sugar. Cook for 2 minutes. Add the cold water and egg yolk. Cook gently, stirring until the mixture thickens. Chill. Fold in whipped cream and vanilla before serving.

# EDINBURGH DELIGHT

Add one or two teaspoons of butterscotch sauce to a serving of lemon water ice. Coat with Drambuie and decorate with whipped cream.

# *PUDDINGS*

## CLOOTIE DUMPLING

| METRIC | IMPERIAL |
|---|---|
| *150 g flour* | *6 oz flour* |
| *½ teaspoon bicarbonate of soda* | *½ teaspoon bicarbonate of soda* |
| *½ teaspoon cinnamon* | *½ teaspoon cinnamon* |
| *½ teaspoon ground ginger* | *½ teaspoon ground ginger* |
| *pinch of salt* | *pinch of salt* |
| *75 g beef suet (finely chopped)* | *3 oz beef suet (finely chopped)* |
| *100 g currants* | *4 oz currants* |
| *50 g sultanas* | *2 oz sultanas* |
| *75 g sugar* | *3 oz sugar* |
| *grated rind of 1 orange* | *grated rind of 1 orange* |
| *milk to mix* | *milk to mix* |

Sift the flour, baking powder and spices together. Add all the other dry ingredients to the flour mixture and mix well. Add enough milk to make a stiff dough. Place in a heatproof basin leaving room for the pudding to swell. Cover with greaseproof paper and seal with kitchen foil. Place in a large saucepan of hot water and boil for 4 hours. Make sure that the water does not reach the top of the basin: keep topping it up. Serve hot with custard.

## APPLE AMBER PUDDING

| METRIC | IMPERIAL |
|---|---|
| *400 g cooking apples (peeled, cored and sliced)* | *1 lb cooking apples (peeled, cored and sliced)* |
| *75 g sugar* | *3 oz sugar* |
| *2 egg yolks* | *2 egg yolks* |
| *shortcrust pastry (See page 18)* | *shortcrust pastry (See page 18)* |
| *grated rind and juice of ½ lemon* | *grated rind and juice of ½ lemon* |

| *Meringue* | *Meringue* |
|---|---|
| *75 g caster sugar* | *3 oz caster sugar* |
| *2 egg whites* | *2 egg whites* |

Line a flan tin with shortcrust pastry. Brush with a little egg white, prick and bake blind. Add the lemon rind and lemon juice to the apples. Mix and add sugar to taste. Add a little water and boil gently until the fruit is is just soft. Remove from the heat and allow to cool. Stir in the egg yolks. Pour the apple mixture into the baked flan case. Bake in a moderate oven (170°C, 350°F, gas mark 4) for 35 minutes until the mixture is set.

**Meringue** Whisk the egg whites until they stand up in peaks. Fold in the caster sugar. Pile the meringue on top of the apple mixture and bake in a cool oven (150°C, 300°F, gas mark 2) until it is lightly browned. Serve hot or cold.

# JAM SPONGE PUDDING

| METRIC | IMPERIAL |
|---|---|
| *75 g butter* | *3 oz butter* |
| *75 g caster sugar* | *3 oz caster sugar* |
| *1 egg (beaten)* | *1 egg (beaten)* |
| *150 g self raising flour* | *5 oz self raising flour* |
| *2 drops vanilla essence* | *2 drops vanilla essence* |
| *1 tablespoon milk* | *1 tablespoon milk* |
| *3 tablespoons raspberry or strawberry jam* | *3 tablespoons raspberry or strawberry ja* |

Cream the butter amd sugar together until light and fluffy. Add the egg a little at a time beating after each addition. Sift the flour and then fold into the creamed mixture. Add the essence and a little milk to give a dropping consistency. Grease a 600 - 900 ml (1 - 1½ pint) pie dish. Spread the jam over the bottom of the dish. Put the pudding mixture into the dish on top of the jam. Bake in a moderate oven (170°C, 350°F, gas mark 4) for 30 - 40 minutes until well risen and golden. Serve with a jam sauce or custard or cream.

# SPICY FRUIT SPONGE

Sift a teaspoon of mixed spice with the flour. Add 75 g (3 oz) sultanas or currants when folding in the flour.

# *PRESERVES*

## THREE FRUIT MARMALADE

METRIC
*2 sweet oranges*
*4 lemons*
*2 grapefruit*
*3•4 litres water*
*1•3 kg sugar*

IMPERIAL
*2 sweet oranges*
*4 lemons*
*2 grapefruit*
*6 pints water*
*3 lb sugar*

Wash the lemons and oranges. Cut in half and squeeze out the juice and pips. Wash and peel the grapefruit. Remove any thick white pith. Tie pith and pips in muslin. Cut all the peel thickly and the flesh roughly. Put the peel, fruit pulp, juice and water with the muslin bag containing pith and pips in a large saucepan. Simmer gently for about 1 - 1½ hours until the peel is really soft and the contents of the pan are reduced by at least a third. Remove the bag of pips, squeezing well. Add the sugar and stir until it has dissolved. Boil rapidly until setting point is reached. Leave to stand for 15 minutes. Pot in sterilized jars and seal.

## MIXED VEGETABLE RELISH

METRIC
*1 kg mixed vegetables (prepared)*
*salt*
*spiced vinegar*

IMPERIAL
*2 lb mixed vegtables (prepared)*
*salt*
*spiced vinegar*

Suitable vegetables include cauliflower, small cucumbers, shallots, French beans. Break the cauliflower into florets, peel and dice the cucumbers, peel the shallots, cut up the beans. Place the vegetables in a bowl, sprinkle with salt and cover with water. Leave overnight. Drain off the salt water, rinse the vegetables well and dry with a cloth. Pack into jars and cover with cold, spiced vinegar. Seal the jars and leave for at least a month before using.

# PEAR CHUTNEY

METRIC
*1•5 kg pears (peeled, cored and sliced)*
*450 g onions (skinned and chopped)*
*450 g green tomatoes (sliced)*
*225 g stoned raisins (chopped)*
*700 g demerara sugar*
*¼ teaspoon cayenne*
*¼ teaspoon ground ginger*
*2 teaspoons salt*
*5 peppercorns in a muslin bag*
*1 litre malt vinegar*

IMPERIAL
*3 lb pears (peeled, cored and sliced)*
*1 lb onions (skinned and chopped)*
*1 lb green tomatoes (sliced)*
*8 oz stoned raisins (chopped)*
*1 ½ lb demerara sugar*
*¼ teaspoon cayenne*
*¼ teaspoon ground ginger*
*2 teaspoons salt*
*5 peppercorns in a muslin bag*
*1 ¾ pints malt vinegar*

Put all the fruit and vegetables into a pan with no added liquid and simmer until tender. Add the remaining ingredients and simmer until the mixture is thick with no excess liquid. Remove the bag of peppercorns. Pot in sterilized jars and seal.

# INDEX